TEEN Health

COURSE 3

Health Labs

AUTHOR
Linda Lundgren
Biology Teacher
Bear Creek High School
Lakewood, Colorado

Glencoe
McGraw-Hill

New York, New York   Columbus, Ohio   Woodland Hills, California   Peoria, Illinois

Glencoe/McGraw-Hill

A Division of The McGraw-Hill Companies

Send all inquiries to:
Glencoe/McGraw-Hill
21600 Oxnard Street, Suite 500
Woodland Hills, CA 91367

ISBN 0-02-653218-2   Health Labs

Printed in the United States of America.

3 4 5 6 7 8 9   045   04 03 02 01 00

Table of Contents

Introduction

In an age of high technology, it is important for students to acquire skills related to scientific methods. These Health Labs will give students experience with making observations and hypotheses, collecting and recording data, and forming conclusions based on analysis and interpretations of experimental results. Scientific literacy, scientific principles, and scientific inquiry are developed. Students will increase their science vocabulary, learn how to handle laboratory equipment, use modern laboratory techniques, and acquire skill in working with tables and graphs.

The *Teen Health* Health Labs follow the sequence of chapters in the text and reinforce concepts presented in those chapters. There is one Health Lab activity for each chapter of the student text, keyed to a particular lesson. For each lab, there is a teacher page followed by one or more student pages.

The activities in this manual are presented as scientific problems. Through the use of scientific methods, the students seek answers. Conclusions are based on observations, or experimental data, and analysis of these data and observations.

You say you have never taught science before? This manual assumes no prior scientific background on the part of the teacher. The logical organization, clear explanations, and ease of experimental work will ensure success for both you and your students.

Helpful teaching strategies and safety and disposal guidelines are outlined on the teacher pages. The teacher pages also provide instructions for preparation of solutions, time allotments, answers to questions, sample data, teaching tips, cooperative learning suggestions, sources of materials, and alternative materials.

Equipment needs are simple; suggestions are made for borrowing equipment from a science classroom. Chemicals and other materials can usually be purchased from grocery stores; and scientific supply houses are recommended for purchase of some limited materials.

Teacher Pages

The teacher pages are organized as follows:
Objectives: You may want to use these performance objectives as a basis for evaluating student progress.
Materials: Equipment and supplies for each activity are listed here.
Time: Time allotments for the complete activity are given here.
Preparation: Information about what you need to do to get ready, what equipment to borrow, materials to purchase, and alternative procedures and materials are listed here.
Safety: Specific safety considerations are addressed here.
Teaching the Lab: Teaching tips, reminders for students, and suggestions for methods such as cooperative learning are given in this section.
Sample Hypothesis: A sample of a likely student hypothesis statement is given here.
Sample Data: Any sample data available are presented here.
Analysis: Sample answers to discussion questions that appear on the student pages are provided here.
Further Investigation: Possible future investigations based on what students have learned are given here.

Student Pages

The format of each lab activity is outlined below.
Introduction: A brief introduction provides background information. The introduction is designed to motivate and inform.
Objectives: These statements are performance objectives. Students can use them to determine what they will be doing and what is important in the activity.

Materials: Equipment and supplies for each activity are listed here. Quantities listed will be enough for individuals or groups, as appropriate.

Procedure: Instructions are listed step by step. Strong emphasis is placed on developing the students' skills in carefully following directions, observing, measuring, and recording data in an organized manner.

Hypothesis: A hypothesis is an educated guess about what might happen. Students are asked to express their expectations in hypothesis statements.

Data and Observations: Data or tables may be presented, or students may be expected to record their own data and observations.

Analysis: Discussion questions occur at the end of each activity. These questions review the main ideas, direct attention to key parts of the procedure, and relate the material to the concepts and applications.

Further Investigation: Students will be asked to think about how they could expand on what they have discovered.

Lab Safety

The activities in the *Teen Health* Health Labs are designed to minimize dangers in the lab. There are no guarantees against accidents. However, careful planning and preparation as well as being aware of hazards can help keep accidents to a minimum. Numerous books and pamphlets are available on lab safety. Much of what they present can be summarized in the phrase "Be prepared!" Know the rules and what common violations occur. Know where emergency equipment is stored and how to use it. Practice good lab housekeeping and management by observing these guidelines:

1. Store chemicals and equipment properly.
2. Provide adequate work space for students. Ask students to keep their books, coats, and other materials away from their work space.
3. Provide adequate room ventilation.
4. Post safety and evacuation guidelines.
5. Check to ensure that safety equipment is accessible and working properly. Ideally, safety equipment should include fire extinguishers, fire blankets, and eyewash stations. Review the use of these items.
6. Provide containers for disposing of chemicals and other waste products. Discuss disposal and cleanup procedures.
7. Use hot plates for activities requiring a heat source. Be sure the room has an adequate number of electrical outlets, and use only UL-approved extension cords. Never use open flames when a flammable solvent is in the same room. Thus, alcohol burners should not be used; alcohol in the presence of fire is a potentially dangerous situation.
8. Before beginning each activity, review the procedure and emphasize the cautions. Review what students should do if an accident occurs.
9. Perform each activity yourself before assigning it to students to determine where students may have trouble.
10. Prohibit eating and drinking in the lab.
11. Be sure that hot plates and burners are turned off when not in use.
12. Insist that all students wash their hands when lab work is completed.

Teaching the Health Lab

Use with Chapter 1, Lesson 2.

Promoting Good Health

Objectives
- Hypothesize the class level of wellness.
- Construct a class wellness continuum.
- Analyze the factors that may have affected the continuum results.
- As a group, contribute to a class wellness handbook.

Materials
Newsprint
Index cards
Cardboard box
Drawing paper
Word processing equipment (optional)

Time: Two class periods

Preparation
- Make copies of the student worksheet on page 2, one per student.
- Have volunteers create a number line on newsprint, then reproduce the wellness continuum in the student text along the line.
- Gather art materials for students to use in preparing a health handbook.
- If available, arrange for a computer with word processing software for preparation of the handbook.

Teaching the Lab
1. Display the wellness continuum on a wall of the classroom. Discuss which elements fit into the physical, mental/emotional, or social parts of the health triangle. Then ask students to suggest additional items. Write the items in an appropriate place on the continuum number line.
2. Ask students to hypothesize where on this continuum they think the class average might fall.

3. Give each student an index card. Ask students to write a number on the card that shows where they think they fall on the health continuum. To protect privacy, have students mark the cards individually, then place them face down in a cardboard box.
4. Review the cards. Then place a marker on the continuum that shows the average point for the class. Discuss whether this point comes close to the students' hypothesis.
5. Next, have the class form three groups. Assign *physical, mental/emotional,* or *social* to each group. Encourage groups to create a class health handbook that describes and illustrates lifestyle factors, attitudes, heredity, environment, and behaviors that affect the parts of the health triangle. Have them list their own ideas for improvement, starting with their point on the continuum.
6. Have groups prepare a final copy. Work with the class to decide the order of the material. If possible, make a copy for each student.
7. Have students answer the Analysis questions on the back of their worksheets. Encourage groups to discuss their answers.

Analysis
Answers will vary, depending on students' opinions and the results on the continuum.

Further Investigation
Invite groups to use the school wellness survey conducted in their textbook to plan an advertisement for the class health handbook. Provide several copies of the handbook for students to present to other classes.

Health Lab

Use with Chapter 1, Lesson 2.

Promoting Good Health

Introduction

Many people are confused by what it means to be healthy. They may have no idea what parts of their health need improving or what they could do if they knew where help was needed. Young people are no exception. In fact, some young people may tune out health advice, thinking it doesn't apply to them because it comes from adults. This is where young people can help one another.

Objectives

- Hypothesize the class level of wellness.
- Construct a class wellness continuum.
- Analyze the factors that may have affected the continuum results.
- As a group, contribute to a class wellness handbook.

Materials

Index cards
Cardboard box
Drawing paper
Word processing equipment (optional)

Procedure

1. Study the wellness continuum reproduced from your textbook. Talk with your class about which items are a part of the physical, mental/emotional, or social sections of the health triangle. Suggest additional items. As a class, hypothesize at what point on the continuum the class average might fall. What reasons do you have for your choice?
2. Think about your health lifestyle, attitudes, and choices. Honestly decide at what point you might be on the continuum. On an index card, write the corresponding number.
3. Your teacher will mark the continuum to show the average point for the class. Do the results verify your hypothesis? If not, how might you change your hypothesis?

5. Next, join one of three class groups to create a class health handbook. Each group will work on one part of the handbook, covering the physical, mental/emotional, or social section of the health triangle.
6. You can use your textbook for ideas on topics to cover. Discuss with your group how these topics apply to you and what you know about others your age. List ideas on how someone could improve his or her position on the health continuum.
7. Write or use a computer to prepare final copy for your group's part of the handbook. Illustrate your copy with drawings, charts, or photos. As a class, decide the order in which you want to put the information in your handbook.
8. Write answers to the Analysis questions that follow. Discuss your answers with your group.

Analysis

1. Based on the point where the class falls on the wellness continuum, what can you conclude about the attitudes young people have about their health?
2. What factors might affect the results on the wellness continuum, such as personal choice, health habits, peer pressure, and media influences?
3. What do you think are the most important ideas about health that young people need to take seriously?
4. How might young people convince their peers to change bad health habits?

Further Investigation

How might your class health handbook be useful for other students? How would you advertise it?

Activity 2 Teaching the Health Lab

Use with Chapter 2, Lesson 2.

Do Mouthwashes Really Work?

Objectives
- Test the effectiveness of mouthwashes in killing mouth bacteria.
- Compare the effectiveness of mouthwashes to the effectiveness of saltwater solution in killing mouth bacteria.

Materials
A variety of mouthwashes (students may bring them from home)
Small paper cups, 1 per student
Disposable petri dishes prepared with nutrient agar, 1 per student
Masking tape
Sterile toothpicks, 3 per student
Salt solution, 1 quart per class
Graph paper
Calculators (optional on second day)

Time: Two class periods

Preparation
- Make copies of the student worksheets on pages 4 and 5, one per student.
- Order prepared disposable nutrient agar petri dishes from a supply house, or get them from the science department.
- Sterilize toothpicks by wrapping them in aluminum foil and autoclaving. If an autoclave is not available, rinse them in alcohol. Use fresh toothpicks for each class.
- Prepare salt solution by stirring 2 teaspoons of salt into a quart of warm water.
- On the second day of the lab, put a chart on the board similar to the one on the student page. Allow space for all student results.
- Have the petri dishes autoclaved before disposing of them. If an autoclave is not available, petri dishes can be sterilized in a dishwasher.
- If an incubator is not available, incubate the dishes for 3 to 5 days in a warm spot, such as under a desk lamp with a high-intensity bulb. Check each day for growth.

Bacteria colonies will be small round spots on the agar. Some will be pinpoint size, some as large as a dime. Some will be raised; some will be shades of white, cream, tan, yellow, and other colors.

Safety
1. Students should not swallow mouthwash or salt solution.
2. Students should use sterile technique as outlined here.
   A. Touch only one end of the toothpick.
   B. Do not touch the inside of the petri dish or cover during inoculation.
   C. Do not open petri dishes after incubation.

Teaching the Lab
1. Review the safety precautions and procedure with the students.
2. You might wish to allow students to practice the inoculation technique before carrying out their own experiments.

Sample Hypothesis: All of the sections of the dish will have equal numbers of bacteria colonies.

Sample Data
Number of bacteria colonies will be approximately the same in each section. The salt solution may inhibit some growth.

Analysis
1. Answers will vary, but the average for all sections will be about the same.
2. Answers will vary.
3. No.
4. Most likely not, but maybe a little better than mouthwash.
5. Brushing and flossing.

Further Investigation
Carry out the same tests after brushing and flossing teeth.

Teen Health • Course 3 • Health Labs   **3**

Health Lab

Activity 2

Do Mouthwashes Really Work?

Introduction

Freshen your breath; kill germs; prevent colds; reduce plaque; clean your mouth. Advertisements for mouthwashes promise to ensure healthy mouths, teeth, and gums. Some studies show that the effectiveness of most of these products matches that of a breath mint. There may be some benefit in cavity prevention in mouthwashes with fluoride, but antiplaque prerinses have not been proven effective. In this lab, you will study the effectiveness of mouthwashes in killing bacteria in the mouth.

Objectives
- Test the effectiveness of mouthwashes in killing mouth bacteria.
- Compare the effectiveness of mouthwashes to the effectiveness of saltwater solution in killing mouth bacteria.

Materials
A variety of mouthwashes
Small paper cup, 1 per student
Disposable petri dish prepared with nutrient agar, 1 per student
Masking tape
Sterile toothpicks, 3 per student
Salt solution
Graph paper

Procedure

PART A: DAY 1
1. Without opening your petri dish, make three lines on the bottom of the dish that divide it into three equal parts.
2. With a sterile toothpick, gently scrape the inside of your cheek and the side of a back tooth. Do not touch that end of the toothpick to anything else before or after scraping.

3. Take the cover off the petri dish. Do not touch the inside of the dish.
4. Being careful not to cut into the surface of the agar, gently run the toothpick back and forth across the surface in one of the three sections. You should not be able to see the line on the surface of the agar. Dispose of the toothpick in a trash receptacle as indicated by your teacher.
5. Cover the dish. Mark that section of the bottom of the dish with an *N* for normal.
6. Pour the amount of mouthwash recommended for use into a paper cup. Use as directed on the bottle. Do not swallow mouthwash.
7. With another sterile toothpick, repeat step 4, and then run the toothpick over another section of agar. Mark the bottom of that section *M* for mouthwash.
8. Rinse your cup thoroughly, and pour a small amount of saltwater solution into it. Rinse your mouth in the same manner as you did with the mouthwash.
9. With another sterile toothpick, repeat step 4, and then run the toothpick over the last section of agar. Mark the bottom of that section *S* for salt.
10. Seal your petri dish with masking tape all the way around the edge. Do not put tape across the top or bottom of the dish. Write your name on the tape.
11. Make a hypothesis as to which section will grow the fewest bacteria.
12. Give the petri dish to your teacher for incubation.

PART B: DAY 2
13. Do not open your petri dish. Disease-causing bacteria may now be growing on the agar.

Health Lab • Activity 2   (continued)

14. Count the number of bacteria colonies in each section of the dish. Write the number on the chart on the board.

15. Average the class data by adding the number of colonies in each section and dividing by the number of students in the class. Write the class averages in Table 1 in the Data and Observations section.

Data and Observations

Table 1

Section of Petri Dish	Average Number of Bacteria Colonies
Normal	
Mouthwash	
Salt Solution	

16. Make a bar graph on your graph paper. On the horizontal axis, write the conditions you tested: normal, mouthwash, salt solution. The vertical axis will have the average numbers of colonies.

Analysis

1. Which section of your dish had the fewest bacteria colonies? How did this compare to the class average?

2. Which section of your dish had the most bacteria colonies? How did this compare to the class average?

3. According to the class results, does mouthwash kill bacteria? Explain your answer.

4. According to class results, does salt solution kill bacteria?

5. What would be a more effective way to get rid of bacteria in your mouth?

Further Investigation

Based on what you have learned today, how could you expand your experimental work?

Activity 3 Teaching the Health Lab

Use with Chapter 3, Lesson 2.

Can Laughter Help You Learn?

Objectives
• Compare problem-solving ability before and after viewing a comic film.
• Evaluate the value of laughter prior to problem solving.

Materials
Toothpicks, 13 per student
Comic 10-minute film or video
Film projector or video player and monitor

Time: One class period

Preparation
• Make copies of the student worksheet on page 7, one per student.
• Obtain a comic film such as a Bugs Bunny cartoon, or videotape a TV comedy show.

Teaching the Lab
1. Review the procedure with the students.
2. Tell students when their 5-minute time segments for each problem have elapsed.
3. For Problem 3, draw this figure on the board.

4. Provide the additional problems below for those who finish.

Problem 4 (physical) Have students place toothpicks in the shape of this grid. The object is to remove 3 toothpicks to leave 3 triangles.

Problem 5 (logic) Edna, Jerry, and Vera compared their grades for history, English, and math. Each had one A, one B, and one C. Tell what grades the three students received for all three subjects using the following clues:
A. No two students had the same grade for any one subject.
B. Edna's grade for English was lower than Jerry's grade for history, but higher than Vera's grade for math.

Sample Data
Answers will vary. Students may not be able to solve the problems before or after the film, but they will be less frustrated after viewing the film.

Analysis
Answers will vary for questions 1 and 4.
2. Sample answer: After film, less stress, less frustration, able to think of more ways of problem solving.
3. Sample answer: It reduces stress, anxiety, and frustration.

Answers to Problems
1. (This is one of several solutions.)

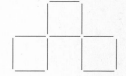

2. Wendy, John, Fred, Rhonda
3. 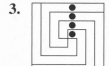   4.

5. Edna: history C, English B, math A
   Jerry: history A, English C, math B
   Vera: history B, English A, math C

Further Investigation
Experiment with different lengths of time for films. Test different kinds of problem solving.

Activity 3 Health Lab

Can Laughter Help You Learn?

Introduction

Recently, scientists found that people who watched a comic film were more creative in solving problems after viewing the film than those who did not have the chance to laugh.

Objectives

- Compare problem-solving ability before and after viewing a comic film.
- Evaluate the value of laughter prior to problem solving.

Materials

Toothpicks, 13 per student

Procedure

PART A

Spend 5 minutes trying to solve each problem below. Note in Table 1 in Data and Observations how long it takes you to solve each problem. Each problem requires a different type of reasoning.

Problem 1 (physical) Place 12 toothpicks on your desk in the shape of a tic-tac-toe grid. Move three toothpicks to form three identical squares.

Problem 2 (logic) Fred, John, Rhonda, and Wendy all baby-sat for neighbors. At the end of the summer, they compared how much they had done. They noticed the following:
a. John baby-sat more than Fred and Rhonda put together.
b. The total of Fred and John's baby-sitting just equaled the amount of Rhonda and Wendy's baby-sitting.
c. The total of Fred and Wendy's baby-sitting was more than the total of John and Rhonda's.
Arrange the names in order from most baby-sitting to least.

Problem 3 (spatial orientation) The owner of an estate had a square piece of property on which were planted four prize-winning rose bushes. The bushes were all in a row and equally spaced. In her will, the owner left the property to her daughters. It was to be divided up into four identical parts, each with its rose bush. Copy the sketch your teacher provides. Solve the problem.

PART B
1. View the film.

PART C
2. If you didn't solve the problems, go back and see if you can do them now. If you solved them, your teacher will give you some new problems. Note how long it takes you to do each one.

Data and Observations

Table 1

Problem	Time to solve before film	Time to solve after film
1		
2		
3		
4		
5		

Analysis
1. Were you able to solve the problems before viewing the film? After the film?
2. Even if you could not solve the problems, was there a difference in how you felt about them before and after the film?
3. How does laughing improve your state of mind?
4. Was it easier for you to solve a physical, a logic, or a spatial orientation problem?

Further Investigation

Based on what you have learned today, how could you expand this experiment?

Rating the Family

Objectives
- Hypothesize how the American family is portrayed on television.
- In a group, analyze television families and compare them to a real family description.
- Compare conclusions with other groups.

Materials
Videotape with selection of television family sitcoms and video player (optional)

Time: Two class periods

Preparation
- Make copies of the student worksheet on page 9, one per student.
- Videotape three or four television family sitcoms, or list several to assign to different groups to view.

Teaching the Lab
1. Review the different types of family structures.
2. Lead a class discussion on how television portrays a typical family and how it might influence people's ideas about families.
3. Help the class create a description of what they consider a real family to be, including relationships, support, problems, and solutions.
4. Have students form small cooperative groups. Assign each group a family sitcom to watch during the week, or show excerpts of videotaped programs to the class or groups. Encourage students to take notes, using the chart on their worksheets.
5. Have groups discuss their ideas and write answers to the Analysis questions on the back of their worksheets.
6. Allow groups an opportunity to compare their ideas with the rest of the class.
7. Have the class conclude whether or not television presents a realistic portrayal of the American family, and why or why not.

Analysis
Answers will vary, depending on the program watched and on students' impressions. Students should use incidents from the program and their own experience to support their answers.

Further Investigation
If students have seen reruns of past programs—such as *The Dick Van Dyke Show, Good Times, Father Knows Best, My Two Dads,* and *Kate and Allie*—discuss how the families portrayed differ from those shown on television today.

Activity 4 Health Lab

Use with Chapter 4, Lesson 3.

Rating the Family

Introduction

Many people believe television provides a mirror of our society. Others feel television shows an unrealistic and stereotyped picture of what people and families are really like, and so creates false expectations and comparisons.

Objectives

• Hypothesize how the American family is portrayed on television.
• In a group, analyze television families, and compare them to a real family description.
• Compare conclusions with other groups.

Materials

Videotape with selection of television family sitcoms and video player (optional)

Procedure

1. Discuss your ideas with your class on how television sitcoms portray families.
2. Create a class description of how you view real families.
3. With your group, view program excerpts your teacher has taped, or view at home the program your teacher assigns to your group. Take notes on how the family is portrayed. On a separate piece of paper, create a chart like the one on this page.

4. Compare your notes with other group members. Use the Analysis questions to compare the television family with your class description of a realistic family.
5. Share your review with other groups.
6. Develop a class conclusion based on your analysis.

Analysis

1. How do the problems of the television family resemble those of a real family?
2. How is humor or drama used to solve these problems? Is this realistic or not?
3. How do the family members relate to one another? Why do you think this is realistic or not realistic?
4. How might this television family influence people's ideas about real families? Do you think this would be a positive or a negative influence?

Further Investigation

How are today's families portrayed differently on television from families in the past?

Name of Program	Kind of Family	Family Members (ages/sex)	Economic Situation	Ethnic Group	Problems Confronted	Solutions

Teaching the Health Lab

Analyzing Violence in the Media

Objectives
- With a group, survey one form of media for the number of violent incidents reported or described.
- Indicate the types of violence reported or described.
- Analyze attitudes toward violence.

Materials
Current news magazines
Current local and national newspapers
Tapes of television news programs

Time: Two class periods

Preparation
- Make copies of the student worksheet on page 11, one per student.
- Collect a variety of current news magazines and newspapers. You may wish to ask students to bring these materials from home.

Teaching the Lab
1. Ask the class to suggest different media through which people view or hear about violence, including television, newspapers, magazines, and music. Discuss ways violence is presented, such as in dramatic shows, music videos, comedy, news reports, personal stories, and talk shows.
2. Tell students they will be focusing on and analyzing violence in one media form: newspapers, news magazines, or television news programs.
3. Have the class form three cooperative groups. Assign each group to one form of media.

4. Suggest that groups conduct their survey over a few days to allow time for reading and watching news programs. Encourage students to use the chart on their worksheets as a guide for their investigation.
5. Have students also look for instances where conflicts are resolved nonviolently. Have them analyze what method of conflict resolution was used in each case. A group may have to follow some news reports for a few days to discover how resolutions were reached.
6. Allow time for groups to analyze and discuss the information they collect. Suggest they write answers to the Analysis questions on the back of their worksheets, and use them to guide their discussion.
7. Invite groups to prepare and present to the class a report on the results of their survey and analysis. Compare the results of the different media.
8. Discuss what the reports suggest about the prevalence of different forms of violence in our society and the attitudes people seem to have toward this violence.

Analysis
Answers will vary, depending on the media form investigated and analyzed.

Further Investigation
Help students research the level of violence in other industrialized countries and compare this with the level of violence in the United States.

Health Lab   **Use with Chapter 5, Lesson 3.**

Analyzing Violence in the Media

Introduction

Some people say that violence in the media is merely a reflection of violence in society. Others claim that the rise in violence in society is directly influenced by what people are exposed to in the media. To focus more clearly on this problem, it may help to analyze how violence is presented in at least one form of the media.

Objectives

- With a group, survey one form of news media for the number of violent incidents reported or described.
- Indicate the types of violence reported or described.
- Analyze attitudes toward violence.

Materials

News magazines, national and local newspapers

Procedure

1. Discuss with your class the media forms through which people are exposed to violence. Talk about the different types of violence portrayed in each form of media. Then focus on how violence is portrayed in newspapers, news magazines, and television news.
2. Your teacher will assign your group a media form to analyze: newspapers, news magazines, or television news programs.
3. Schedule time at home to do your survey, or use classroom materials. Be sure to survey a variety of articles. Count the incidents of each type of violence reported or described, using the chart on this page as a guide.
4. Next count the number of incidents in which violence is avoided through conflict resolution.

5. Meet with your group to talk about your results. Use the Analysis questions to guide your discussion. Develop a conclusion on violence. Then plan a class presentation.

Analysis

1. What types of violence are most prevalent?
2. By what methods were any conflicts resolved or was violence avoided?
3. How does the number of violent incidents reported or described compare to the number of nonviolent incidents covered?
4. What might happen if the media were banned from reporting or describing all forms of violence? Do you think violence would decrease, or would just our perceptions of violence change?

Further Investigation

How does the level of violence in the United States compare with levels in other industrialized countries?

Media Form:				
	Violent Incidents Reported			
Types	**1–5**	**6–10**	**more than 10**	**Violent Incidents Avoided**
Physical violence				
Property damage				
Fear/threat of violence				
Verbal attacks				

Teaching the Health Lab

Do Your Sunglasses Distort Your View?

Objectives
- Test sunglasses for color and shape and line distortion.
- Compare results of tests on sunglasses with group members.

Materials
Box of 64 Crayola crayons, 1 per group
Masking tape
Butcher paper, 1 large sheet per group
Yardstick
Sunglasses, several pairs per group
Black ballpoint pen, 1 per group

Time: One class period

Preparation
- Make copies of the student worksheets on pages 13 and 14, one per student.
- Use this activity after students have completed their study of Lesson 2.
- Ask students to bring in sunglasses to test.

Teaching the Lab
1. Review the procedure with the students.
2. Have students work in small groups of three or four.

Sample Hypothesis: Gray and green lenses distort color the least.

Sample Data
Answers will vary. Shape and line distortion are related to the cost of the sunglasses. Good optical quality sunglasses can be purchased for as little as $10. Gray and green lenses distort color the least for most people. Amber and brown produce some color distortion. Blue and purple produce the most color distortion.

Analysis
1. Answers will vary.
2. Answers will vary.
3. Answers will vary.
4. Gray or green
5. UV protection
6. No
7. $10–$15

Further Investigation
Test sunglasses for shatter resistance, scratch resistance, UV screening, and light absorption.

Health Lab   Use with Chapter 6, Lesson 2.

Do Your Sunglasses Distort Your View?

Introduction

Polarized, UV blocking, glass, plastic, light tint, dark tint, brown, gray, green, gradient, and mirrored. When you shop for sunglasses, these are just a few of the words that will tumble through your mind as you scan the selection. Most important, sunglasses should block the ultraviolet (UV), invisible light from the sun. UV light can cause permanent eye damage. The tint of the lens is not what blocks UV light. Look for a label on the glasses that tells about UV blockage.

Polarized lenses cut down on glare. Glass is more scratch resistant but heavier than plastic. Gradient lenses are darker on top. Mirrored lenses offer more protection against glare, but scratch easily. This lab will show you how to ensure that your next pair of sunglasses does not distort colors or shapes.

Objectives

- Test sunglasses for color and shape and line distortion.
- Compare results of tests on sunglasses with group members.

Materials

Box of 64 Crayola crayons, 1 per group
Masking tape
Butcher paper
Yardstick
Sunglasses, several pairs per group
Black ballpoint pen

Procedure

PART A: SHAPE AND LINE DISTORTION

1. Examine the sunglasses your group has. Make a hypothesis as to which you think will distort color and shape the least.
2. Using a yardstick, draw a straight line 12 inches long on your butcher paper with the ballpoint pen.

3. Tape the paper to the wall so the line is vertical and at eye level. Stand about 20 feet from the paper. The line should be barely visible through sunglasses. If it is *not* visible, move a little closer to the paper.
4. Hold the sunglasses at arm's length directly in front of you. Move the glasses up and down the line very slowly. If the line seems to curve, bend, or sway as you look through the lenses, the lenses are not perfect and will distort shapes when you wear them.
5. Write the data for your group's sunglasses in Table 1 in the Data and Observations section.

PART B: COLOR DISTORTION

1. Put your sunglasses on. Have a partner hold up two crayons with just the wax tips showing about 18 inches in front of you.
2. Use the list below as a guide as you choose color combinations to test. Select two pairs of colors from each group, and record if you can distinguish the difference between the two colors or if they look the same.
3. Fill in Table 2 for the sunglasses you test.

Color Combinations

1. navy blue, blue, plum, violet, blue violet, royal purple, midnight blue, cerulean, black
2. jungle green, green, pine green, spring green, green yellow
3. mulberry, red violet, wild strawberry, violet red, maroon, fuchsia, magenta, red, brick red
4. bittersweet, brown, burnt orange, mahogany, Indian red, raw sienna, burnt sienna, tan

Health Lab • Activity 6   (continued)

Data and Observations

Table 1

Sunglasses: Shape and Line Distortion
1. Brand name (if known): _____
2. Price (if known): _____
3. Shape and line distortion (present or not present) _____

Table 2

Color Distortion		
Color Group Number	Colors Used	Difference Detected
1		
2		
3		
4		

Analysis

1. Did the straight line appear curved or misshapen through any of the sunglasses tested by your group? What does this mean?
2. Were you able to recognize differences in colors in all groups with your sunglasses? If not, which groups were more difficult to distinguish?
3. Which sunglasses tested by your group had the least color distortion?
4. What color were the lenses of the glasses with which there was the least color distortion? Was it the same for other groups in your class?
5. What is the most important protection offered by sunglasses?

6. Are more expensive sunglasses more effective in preventing color and shape distortion?
7. Estimate how much an adequate pair of sunglasses should cost.

Further Investigation

Based on what you have learned today, how could you expand your experimental work?

Teaching the Health Lab   Use with Chapter 7, Lesson 3.

Accomplishing Developmental Tasks

Objectives
- Hypothesize several ways to show assistance and support to someone as he or she attempts to master an important developmental task.
- In a group, role-play your hypotheses for the class.
- Predict the outcomes of other groups' role plays.

Materials
Textbooks, 1 per student

Time: One class period

Preparation
- Make copies of the student worksheet on page 16, one per student.
- Use this activity after students have read Lesson 3 in their textbooks.
- Do this activity in the theater or drama room, or clear a larger area in the front of the classroom for the role plays.

Teaching the Lab
1. Briefly review Erik Erikson's eight developmental stages of life.
2. Ask for volunteers for each of the situations. Encourage the volunteers to spend several minutes with their group to assign roles and form a hypothesis for the role play. Hypotheses will vary. For example, for situation #1, students may suggest that if the three older siblings show an interest in the ten-year-old's science project, he or she will feel important. Students may also suggest that if the older siblings talk about similar projects they completed and make suggestions based on their experiences, the ten-year-old will understand that he or she is not alone in the struggle to complete the assignment.

3. Have the audience write any suggestions they had for the role play on the backs of their worksheets. If there are many additional suggestions, encourage a second group to role-play the same situation, taking the suggestions into account.
4. Ask for volunteers from the audience to predict the response of the person in the role play for whom the assistance and support was intended.
5. Have students answer the Analysis questions on the backs of their worksheets.

Analysis
1. Answers will vary. Students might suggest that the ten-year-old will not feel important to siblings and will not think his or her struggles matter to anyone else.
2. Answers will vary. Students might suggest that the three friends will become immune to the people and environment around them if they do not pay attention and take the time to care.
3. Answers will vary. Students might suggest that the toddler will not have confidence in his or her motor abilities and may feel that the world is not a safe and secure place.

Further Investigation
Ask students to relay actual experiences they have had with developing their own set of values and how they have had opportunities to help friends clarify their values.

Health Lab

Accomplishing Developmental Tasks

Introduction

According to Erik Erikson, humans go through eight developmental stages in their lives. Associated with each stage are developmental tasks that need to be accomplished in order for people to continue to grow toward becoming healthy, mature adults. It is important for people to receive the proper assistance and support from family and friends during each developmental stage. There are many ways to help those close to you accomplish the developmental tasks associated with each stage.

Objectives

• Hypothesize several ways to show assistance and support as someone attempts to master an important developmental task.

• In a group, role-play your hypotheses for the class.

• Predict the outcomes of other groups' role plays.

Materials

Textbook

Procedure

Work in a group to role-play one of the following life situations. Each situation describes a developmental task associated with a developmental stage. When your group is not role playing, predict the outcomes of the other groups' role plays, and make additional suggestions. Write your suggestions on the other side of this worksheet.

1. The developmental stage is late childhood (6 to 11 years). The developmental task to be mastered is industry—an interest in making things.

    Assume the roles of three older siblings of a ten-year-old. The ten-year-old is struggling to complete a science project. The project is to make a model of a complete flower out of colored construction paper. What can the three older siblings do to help the ten-year-old master the task?

2. The developmental stage is adolescence (11 to 15 years). The developmental task to be mastered is an interest in and concern for the community.

    Assume the roles of three 15-year-old friends. As the three friends are walking home from school, they pass an empty lot full of old newspapers and aluminum cans. What can the three friends do for their community?

3. The developmental stage is early childhood (one to three years). The developmental task to be mastered is autonomy—confidence in one's ability.

    Assume the roles of a mother, a father, and an older sibling of a three-year-old. The three-year-old is busy climbing stairs with the parents' supervision. What can the parents and older sibling do to help the toddler develop confidence?

Analysis

1. What might the outcome of the first situation be if the three older siblings do not show an interest in and provide support to the ten-year-old in his or her endeavors?

2. What might the outcome of the second situation be if the three friends ignore the cluttered lot?

3. What might the outcome of the third situation be if the parents and older sibling of the three-year-old do not exhibit support or confidence in the toddler's attempt to climb the stairs?

Further Investigation

What are some ways that you can encourage and support your classmates as each of you strives to develop a set of your own values?

Activity 8 — Teaching the Health Lab

Use with Chapter 8, Lesson 2.

What Can Heart Rate Tell You About Fitness?

Objectives
- Measure your resting pulse followed by your after-exercise pulse.
- Describe your state of fitness based on the return of your pulse to normal.
- Describe what added weight does to your after-exercise pulse.

Materials
Book bag or backpack, one per student
10 lbs. of books per group
Scale for weighing books

Time: One class period

Preparation
- Tell students to bring a book bag or backpack with extra books to class for this activity.
- Make copies of the student worksheets on pages 18 and 19, one per student.
- This activity may be done as an introduction to or as a review of Chapter 8.
- Tell students to wear comfortable clothing for this lab.
- If your room does not have a clock with a second hand, arrange to have at least one watch with a second hand for every two students.

Safety
1. Students who have knee problems should not do deep knee bends.
2. Exercise immediately after a meal may cause stomach discomfort.

Teaching the Lab
1. Review the safety precautions and procedure with students.
2. Have students work in groups of two.
3. Make sure students do parts A, B, and C in the order prescribed. An accurate resting pulse cannot be taken after exercise.

4. After students complete Table 1, tell them that the average resting pulse for people between 11 and 15 years of age is 60 to 100 beats per minute.
5. If students have come from physical education class, have them rest for at least 6 to 7 minutes before calculating resting pulses.

Sample Hypothesis: My pulse will be higher after exercise with weight than with no added weight.

Sample Data
Table 1 Data will vary.
Table 2 Data will vary.
Table 3 Pulse after jogging for 3 minutes will vary but will increase with added weight.

Analysis
1. Answers will vary, depending on students' state of health, whether they smoke, whether they are under stress, and their state of fitness. Illness or poor health may cause a pulse to be higher. Trained athletes will have lower pulse rates.
2. Answers will vary, depending on state of fitness. Students who engage in regular aerobic exercise will have higher fitness estimates than those who do not.
3. Higher with added weight. The heart must work harder to carry even more food and oxygen to muscle cells that must do more work to carry the added weight.

Further Investigation
   Check heart rate with more weight added. Test other variables, such as temperature, to see if it affects heart rate. Compare heart rates in different positions, such as standing up, lying down, balanced on one leg. Test longer periods of exercise, or different kinds of exercise.

Activity 8

Health Lab

What Can Heart Rate Tell You About Fitness?

Introduction

Your heart pumps blood to every cell in your body. During exercise, your heart rate increases. How much it increases depends not only on the exercise but also on your level of fitness.

Objectives

- Measure your resting pulse, followed by your after-exercise pulse.
- Describe your state of fitness, based on the return of your pulse to normal.
- Describe what added weight does to your after-exercise pulse.

Materials

Book bag or backpack, one per student
10 lbs. of books per group
Scale for weighing books, one per class

Procedure

PART A: RESTING PULSE

1. Count the pulse on your wrist for 20 seconds. Multiply the number of pulses by 3 to find your pulse rate for 1 minute. Repeat this procedure for 4 trials. Record your data in Table 1 in the Data and Observations section. Find your average resting pulse by adding the 4 trials and dividing by 4.

PART B: FITNESS ESTIMATE

2. Do 20 deep knee bends in 40 seconds. Start from a standing position with your arms extended in front of you. Bend your knees so that you end up in a tight squat. Each time you go down counts as one bend.
3. Take your pulse *immediately* after finishing the knee bends. Record the results in Table 2.

4. Rest for 3 minutes. Take your pulse again. Record the results.
5. If your heart rate has not returned to normal, rest for 3 more minutes. Check your pulse again and record.

Fitness Estimate Chart

Average fitness: Pulse is 10 to 20 beats faster after knee bends; returns to normal after 3 minutes.

Above average fitness: Pulse is fewer than 10 beats faster after knee bends; returns to normal after 3 minutes.

Below average fitness: Pulse is more than 20 beats faster after knee bends; returns to normal after 6 minutes.

Poor fitness: Pulse is more than 30 beats faster after knee bends; does not return to normal after 6 minutes.

PART C: EFFECT OF ADDED WEIGHT ON HEART RATE

6. Make a hypothesis about how your pulse will change after exercise with added weight.
7. Jog in place for 3 minutes. Lift your knees high so your thighs are parallel to the floor.
8. Take your pulse immediately after you stop. Record it in Table 3.
9. Put on a backpack or carry a book bag full of books weighing 10 lbs. Jog in place as in step 6, and take your pulse again. Record it in Table 3.

Health Lab • Activity 8   (continued)

Data and Observations

Table 1

Trial	20-Second Pulse	Pulse Rate (beats/min.)
1		
2		
3		
4		
Average resting pulse (beats/min.)		

Table 2

Resting pulse per minute from Part A _____

Pulse per minute immediately after exercise _____

Pulse per minute after resting 3 minutes _____

Pulse per minute after resting 3 more minutes _____

Table 3

Resting pulse per minute from Part A _____

Pulse after jogging for 3 minutes _____

Pulse after jogging for 3 minutes with weight _____

Analysis

1. How does your resting pulse compare to the average resting pulse for someone your age? If it is higher or lower, speculate why.
2. What is your fitness estimate? Why do you think your estimate came out the way it did?
3. Was your pulse rate higher after exercise with or without the added weight? Why?

Further Investigation

Based on what you have learned today, under what other conditions could you measure pulse rate?

Teaching the Health Lab

Use with Chapter 9, Lesson 2.

Choosing a Balanced Diet

Objectives
- Using the Food Guide Pyramid, select food choices for a balanced diet for one day.
- Compare nutrition and ingredients listings on food product labels.
- Determine the number of calories, the number of grams of fat, and the number of milligrams of sodium in the day's food choices.

Materials
Nutrition and ingredients labels from a variety of foods
Food Guide Pyramid Chart (page 267)

Time: One class period

Preparation
- Make a copy of the student worksheet on page 21 for each student in class.
- Ask students to help you collect empty and clean food boxes, cans, and packages, or labels from these packages. If just labels are collected, write the product name on each label. Include a variety of products, such as breads, cereals, soups, canned meats, fruits, vegetables, frozen foods, dairy products, drinks, and fresh meats.
- Inquire at local fast-food restaurants about obtaining nutritional information.
- Create a display of the products or labels, grouping similar foods.

Teaching the Lab
1. Review with students the Food Guide Pyramid and the number of calories, grams of fat, and milligrams of salt recommended each day. (Use the information in Chapter 9.)
2. Discuss food ingredients that many people want to reduce in their diets, including sugar, fats, and salt. Talk about different terms used for these ingredients, such as *dextrose, sucrose, glucose, fructose,*

aspartame (artificial sweetener), corn syrup, oil, and *sodium.*
3. Have students form small groups. Encourage each group to plan a day's menu, from their labels, of food choices for three meals and two snacks. The menu should be based on the suggested servings in the Food Guide Pyramid.
4. Ask each group to use their labels to determine the number of calories and the amount of fat and sodium in their meals and to record the results on their worksheets. Have students compare their totals with the daily amounts suggested in the text (calories: 2,000; fat: 65 grams; sodium: 2,400 milligrams).
5. Have groups write answers to the Analysis questions on the back of their worksheets.
6. Allow groups an opportunity to discuss their results and ideas. Ask: How important is it to read labels in order to maintain a balanced diet? Why should we use the Food Guide Pyramid to help us maintain a balanced diet?

Analysis
Answers will vary, depending on labels selected and students' investigations.

Further Investigation
Help students investigate the meaning of other terms found on food package labels, such as *lite, enriched, artificially sweetened, no preservatives added, cholesterol free, low fat, nonfat, imitation flavors, natural, organic, fresh.* Encourage students to list food additives in products and to investigate their uses—including sweeteners, thickeners, preservatives, coloring agents, flavor enhancers, and bleaching agents. A possible library resource is *The Mount Sinai School of Medicine Complete Book of Nutrition* (St. Martin's Press, 1990).

Activity 9 Health Lab

Choosing a Balanced Diet

Introduction

A trip to the grocery store can be confusing. Shoppers are faced with a bewildering choice of products and packages as food manufacturers attempt to convince consumers that their products are the best and the healthiest. Consumers can make wise choices if they know the information that labels contain and how to use this information.

Objectives

- Using the Food Guide Pyramid, select food choices for a balanced diet for one day.
- Compare nutrition and ingredients listings on food product labels.
- Determine the number of calories, the number of grams of fat, and the number of milligrams of sodium in the day's food choices.

Materials

Nutrition and ingredients labels from a variety of foods
Food Guide Pyramid Chart (page 267)

Procedure

1. With your group, select food labels to use in planning a day's menu of three meals and two snacks.
2. Determine the number of servings of each food by using the number of suggested servings from the Food Guide Pyramid. Use the labels to list calories and amounts of fat and sodium for each food. Write the food choices and numbers on the chart.
3. Write answers to the Analysis questions on the back of this worksheet.

Analysis

1. If you were to eat the menu you chose, how many grams of fat would you consume? How close is this to the recommended 65 grams?
2. How many milligrams of sodium are in your day's menu? How does the amount of sodium in fresh foods compare with the amount in canned foods?

Further Investigation

What other terms do you see on food packages? Which ingredients are food additives? What is their purpose?

Analyzing a Day's Menu

Meal	Food (with number of servings)	Food Pyramid Group	Calories per serving	Grams of fat per serving	Milligrams of sodium per serving
Breakfast					
Lunch					
Afterschool Snack					
Dinner					
Evening Snack					
Totals					

Teaching the Health Lab

Investigating Antacids

Objectives
- Test substances to determine if they are acids or bases.
- Treat acids with antacid products.
- Retest acid substances.

Materials
Small head red cabbage to make acid/base indicator
Small saucepan and strainer
Stove or hot plate
Large jar
Acids and bases, such as lemon juice, baking soda, vinegar, liquid soap, milk
Water
Small jars, glasses, or saucers
Brands of antacids, 1 per group

Time: One class period

Preparation
- You may want to make your own acid indicator at home in order to save time. Place torn leaves of raw cabbage in a small saucepan. Pour water over the leaves, and simmer them on the stove or a hot plate for 15 minutes. Then strain the liquid into a large jar. Make enough for each group to have a small amount.
- Make a copy of the student worksheet on page 23 for each student in class.
- Collect several different brands of antacids.
- Lay out different substances and equipment on tables.

Teaching the Lab
1. Ask the students to name some of the different products available for settling indigestion or heartburn. Remind students that these products work by neutralizing stomach acids.
2. Have the class form small cooperative groups. Provide each group with an antacid, a small jar of cabbage water to use as an indicator, and clean and empty jars or saucers.
3. Review with students that an acid is a corrosive material that eats away other substances. Explain that the opposite of an acid is a base. Mention that before a variety of antacids were available, people often took bicarbonate of soda (a base) and water to neutralize an acid stomach, or to relieve indigestion.
4. Invite groups to test substances such as lemon juice, baking soda, vinegar, liquid soap, and milk to determine if they are acids or bases. Have groups place a small amount of each substance in a jar, then add a small amount of the indicator. Acids turn the indicator red, while bases turn it green.
5. Then have each group add a small amount of antacid to one acid. Suggest they retest the substance with the indicator to see if it still registers as an acid.
6. Have groups write answers to the Analysis questions on the back of their worksheets.
7. Allow groups an opportunity to discuss their results and ideas. Ask: How effective do you think antacids are in neutralizing stomach acids?

Analysis
Answers will vary, depending on the antacid selected and the results of students' investigations.

Further Investigation
Encourage students to investigate home remedies for minor stomach disorders. Suggest they question family members and friends.

Investigating Antacids

Introduction

Having an upset stomach is painful and uncomfortable. A visit to a pharmacy reveals a wide variety of remedies available. According to antacid advertisements, these products bring instant relief for stomach pain. However, some antacids may be more effective than others, and how they work is a mystery to many.

Objectives

- Test substances to determine if they are acids or bases.
- Treat acids with antacid products.
- Retest acid substances.

Materials

Indicator to test acids and bases
Lemon juice
Baking soda
Vinegar
Liquid soap
Milk
Water
Small jars, glasses, or saucers
Brand of antacid

Procedure

1. Your teacher will provide your group with an amount of cabbage water to use as an indicator to test substances to see if they are acids or bases.
2. Place a small amount of the substances you will test in separate jars or saucers. Then add a small amount of your indicator, and observe what happens.

Acids should turn the indicator red, and bases should turn it green. Keep a record of which substances are acids and which are bases.
3. Follow any directions necessary to prepare the antacid your teacher provides, such as dissolving a tablet or powder in water.
4. Add a small amount of the antacid to one of the substances you determined to be an acid.
5. Then use your indicator again to test the substance for any remnants of acid.
6. Share and compare the results of your test with those of other groups.

Analysis

1. What happened when you added the indicator to an acid?
2. What happened when you added the indicator to a base?
3. What happened when you added the indicator to the substance treated with the antacid?
4. How did you know if the antacid had neutralized the acid?
5. How would you judge the effectiveness of the antacid you tested?

Further Investigation

Besides commercial antacids, what home remedies for treating an upset stomach do people use now or have they used in the past?

Teaching the Health Lab
Use with Chapter 11, Lesson 1.

Which Cleaning Products Kill Bacteria?

Objectives
- Test the ability of cleaning products to kill a normal human bacterium.
- Compare the results of tests of various cleaning products in killing bacteria.

Materials
Disposable petri dish cultures of agar with *E. Coli* growth, 1 per group
6 different cleaning products in proper dilution in small beakers or jars
Forceps, 1 per group
Paper towel "punches," 6 per group
Masking tape
Ruler, 1 per group

Time: Two class periods

Preparation
- Make copies of the student worksheets on pages 25 and 26, one per student.
- Order prepared petri dishes inoculated with *E. Coli* from a supply company. A local hospital may provide them free of charge. Keep cultures refrigerated before use.
- Obtain cleaning products. Use bleach, ammonia, Lysol (the kind in the brown bottle), a dishwashing liquid, laundry detergent, and a liquid all-purpose cleaner. Dilute them according to package directions. Note that the Lysol, in particular, is recommended because it will give the best results. Prepare the solutions just before the lab.
- Prepare paper towel punches with a standard paper punch. Place them in solutions just prior to lab.
- Explain that *E. Coli* is a bacterium that normally lives in the human intestines. Ordinarily it does not cause disease. If it gets into another part of the body, such as the bladder, it can, however, cause infection. The chance of this happening during class is very unlikely.

- Autoclave petri dishes before disposal.
- If an incubator is not available, incubate the dishes for 3 to 5 days in a warm spot. Check them each day for clear zones.

Safety
1. Students should wash hands thoroughly at the end of the lab.
2. Students should use careful microbiological technique, as outlined here.
   A. Do not touch the tip of the forceps or touch the inside of the petri dish.
   B. Do not open dishes after incubation.
   C. Do not touch the paper punches with fingers at any time.

Teaching the Lab
1. Review the safety precautions and procedure with the students.
2. Remind students not to move a paper punch once it is on the agar.

Sample Hypothesis: Lysol will kill the most bacteria.

Sample Data
Clear zones—1 mm to 3 cm in diameter. Lysol will have largest zone, followed by ammonia and bleach. Detergents may not produce any clear zones.

Analysis
1. Presence and/or size of clear zone
2. Lysol; answers will vary.
3. Lysol
4. Product with smallest clear zone
5. Answers will vary; probably yes.
6. The punch soaked in water
7. That product does not kill bacteria.
8. It allows bacteria to grow and gives cleaning product time to inhibit growth.

Further Investigation
Use other cleaning products. Use stronger or weaker dilutions.

Activity 11 Health Lab

Use with Chapter 11, Lesson 1.

Which Cleaning Products Kill Bacteria?

Introduction

Cleans and deodorizes. Disinfects. Reduces the spread of household germs. These statements on the packaging of household cleaners suggest that the products kill bacteria. As a result, disease will not spread. In this lab, you will test a common human intestinal bacterium to see if the claims are true. *E. Coli* is a normal harmless bacterial inhabitant of the intestine.

Objectives

- Test the ability of cleaning products to kill a normal human bacterium.
- Compare the results of tests of various cleaning products in killing bacteria.

Materials

Disposable petri dish cultures of agar with *E. Coli* growth, 1 per group
Forceps, 1 per group
Masking tape
Ruler

Procedure

PART A: DAY 1

1. Open your petri dish culture only to place a paper towel "punch" on the surface of the agar. Be careful not to touch the agar or the inside of the dish.
2. With a marker, write on the bottom of your petri dish letters that represent the products you are testing. Write the letters and the products in Table 1 in the Data and Observations section.
3. With clean forceps, select from each beaker one paper towel punch that has been soaking in cleaning product. Place it gently on the surface of the agar over

the appropriate letter. One punch has been soaked only in water. It will serve as your control, or basis of comparison.
4. Place the other punches as directed in Step 3, rinsing the forceps in water carefully after each placement.
5. Space your punches as evenly as possible in your dish. If one lands too close to another, however, leave it there; you do not want to spread that cleaning product to other areas of the dish.
6. Wrap a piece of masking tape around the edges of the petri dish. Write the names of your group members on the tape.
7. Give your dish to your teacher for incubation.
8. Wash your hands thoroughly.
9. Make a hypothesis as to which cleaning product will kill bacteria.

PART B: DAY 2

10. After incubation, do not open your dish.
11. Look for clear zones surrounding the paper punches. You will be able to see most clearly if you hold the dish up to the light. The cleaning products prevented bacterial growth in these clear zones.
12. Measure in millimeters the diameter of each clear zone. Record it in Table 1.

Health Lab • Activity 11   (continued)

Data and Observations

Table 1

Cleaning Product	Letter	Diameter of Clear Zone
water		

Analysis

1. How were you able to tell if a cleaning product stopped or slowed bacterial growth?

2. Which cleaning product has the largest clear zone? The smallest clear zone?

3. Which cleaning product is the most effective in stopping growth of *E. Coli?*
4. Which is least effective in stopping growth of *E. Coli?*
5. Do you think your results would be the same if you used a different bacterium? Why?
6. What proof do you have that the paper punch itself does not prevent bacterial growth?
7. If you had a product with no clear zone after incubation, what would this mean?
8. What is the purpose of incubation?

Further Investigation

Based on what you have learned today, how could you expand your experimental work?

Activity 12

Teaching the Health Lab

Use with Chapter 12, Lesson 1.

Learning to Relax

Objectives
- Discuss the effects of stress.
- Practice relaxation techniques.
- Analyze physical and mental states before and after using relaxation techniques.

Materials
Towels or mats for lying on the floor (optional)

Time: One class period

Preparation
- Make copies of the student worksheet on page 28, one per student.
- Collect mats for students to use for lying on the floor, or ask students to bring a towel from home.

Teaching the Lab
1. Before students know they are to do this health lab, announce a surprise test, oral report, or another activity that might cause an increase in anxiety.
2. Ask the class if your announcement caused tension or stress. Review the definition of stress. Then invite students to suggest ways in which stress is felt physically and mentally. Talk about the different noncommunicable diseases that can be aggravated by stress, such as high blood pressure, heart disease, and asthma.
3. Encourage students to share what they know about relaxation techniques. Invite

them to read through the exercises on their worksheets.
4. If you wish to have students lie on the floor, provide mats or towels. Otherwise have students sit comfortably in their chairs with feet flat on the floor and eyes closed.
5. Start by having students tense their bodies, hold for a few seconds, then relax. Ask them to notice the difference. Have them do the same with just their facial muscles. Instruct them to concentrate on relaxing their jaws, mouths, and eyes. Then talk students through the other exercises on the worksheet.
6. Once the relaxation techniques have been completed, students should answer the Analysis questions on the back of their worksheets. As a class, discuss their answers and ideas. Ask: How might regular use of relaxation techniques help to prevent some noncommunicable diseases?

Analysis
Answers will vary, depending on students' experiences with the exercises.

Further Investigation
Help students research additional relaxation techniques. Discuss how these techniques are similar and different.

Activity 12 Health Lab

Learning to Relax

Introduction

For many people, tension and stress are part of everyday life in our fast-moving society. Those who are used to stress often forget what it feels like to relax. They also pay little attention to the damage stress can cause their bodies until it is too late. By learning just a few relaxation techniques, stress can be reduced and managed.

Objectives

• Discuss the effects of stress.
• Practice relaxation techniques.
• Analyze physical and mental states before and after using relaxation techniques.

Materials

Towel or mat (optional)

Procedure

1. Think about how you felt when your teacher announced the surprise activity. What parts of you became tense and anxious?
2. Read the relaxation techniques described on this page. Then make yourself comfortable in your chair or lying on a floor mat. Close your eyes, and listen as your teacher tells you how to do each exercise.
3. When you are finished, write answers to the Analysis questions on the back of this worksheet. Share your answers with the rest of the class.

Relaxation Techniques

1. *Face:* Tighten your facial muscles. Then relax them all at once. Focus on your jaw, mouth, and eyes, and consciously relax the muscles.

2. *Neck:* Gently roll the neck from side to side. Then roll your head all the way around from side to front to back. Pause in each position and let your muscles relax.
3. *Arms and Hands:* Stretch out your arms, hands, and fingers as far as you can. Then relax them, shake the fingers, and let the arms drop. Do this three or four times.
4. *Legs and Feet:* Stretch out your legs and point your toes. Tense the muscles, then relax them.
5. *Breathing:* Take several slow, deep breaths. Hold your breath for a few seconds, then let it out slowly. Do this a few times.

Analysis

1. How did your muscles feel when you tensed them? How might they feel if you held them that way for a while?
2. How did your muscles feel when you relaxed them? Did you find any leftover tension when you concentrated on individual muscles?
3. How did you feel after you did all of the exercises? How might your outlook change if you did them every day?

Further Investigation

What other techniques have been developed to help people relax?

Activity
13 **Teaching the Health Lab** Use with Chapter 13, Lesson 1.

Do Filters Protect Smokers from Chemicals in Smoke?

Objectives
- Test the effectiveness of filters in removing chemicals from cigarette smoke.
- Measure the amount of chemicals that come through a cigarette filter.

Materials
Test tube, 1 per group
Test tube holder, 1 per group
0.4 g cigarette tobacco (a little less than one cigarette) per group
Cigarette filters (fiber type such as those on Camels), 3 per group
Bunsen burner, 1 per class
Cotton balls, 1 per group
Balance, several for the class
Forceps, thin ones that fit into test tube
Test tube brushes, 1 per group

Time: One class period

Preparation
- Make copies of the student worksheet on page 30, one per student.
- Use this activity as students study Lesson 1.
- If time is a factor, you may wish to weigh the tobacco samples before class.

Safety
1. Students should wear goggles, tie back long hair, and roll up loose sleeves.
2. Caution students about use of test tube holders and cooling the test tube in the rack before touching it.
3. Although not essential, it would be ideal to have all the heating of the tobacco done in a chemical hood if one is available in your classroom.

Teaching the Lab
1. Review the safety precautions and procedure with students.
2. You may want to supervise use of the bunsen burner.
3. Make sure students do not heat the tobacco beyond the blackened point as it will be very difficult to remove from the test tubes.
4. Have students work in groups of three or four. This would be a good lab in which to have students take on assigned cooperative learning roles.

Sample Hypothesis: Filters do not protect smokers from chemicals in smoke.

Sample Data
Gain in weight of cotton will be between 0.02 and 0.1 g.

Analysis
1. It contained chemicals in cigarette smoke.
2. It looks brownish yellow. It is tar and other chemicals.
3. No
4. Yes
5. No

Further Investigation
Test other brands of cigarettes. Test other types of filters. Put more filters on top of those in test tube to see if a longer filter would be better.

Health Lab

Use with Chapter 13, Lesson 1.

Do Filters Protect Smokers from Chemicals in Smoke?

Introduction

The way to avoid health problems associated with smoking is not to smoke and to stay away from other people's cigarette smoke. Tobacco companies advertise that filters protect smokers from the harmful effects of smoking. This lab will demonstrate whether or not this claim is true.

Objectives

- Test the effectiveness of filters in removing chemicals from cigarette smoke.
- Measure the amount of chemicals that come through a cigarette filter.

Materials

Test tube, 1 per group
Test tube holder, 1 per group
Cigarette tobacco
Cigarette filters, 3 per group
Cotton ball, 1 per group
Forceps
Test tube brush, 1 per group

Procedure

1. Weigh 0.4 g of tobacco. Then weigh a cotton ball, and record its weight in Table 1 in the Data and Observations section.
2. Place the weighed tobacco in the test tube.
3. Hold 3 filters together, and push them all at once about one-quarter of the way down into the test tube.
4. Push your cotton ball into the top of the test tube.
5. Make a hypothesis about the ability of filters to screen out chemicals in smoke.
6. Hold your test tube with a test tube holder. Place the bottom of the test tube in the flame until the tobacco turns black and smoke no longer forms. This will take about 30 seconds. Keep the cotton away from the flame, and do not point the test tube toward anyone.

7. Place the test tube in the rack, and wait for it to cool.
8. With forceps, remove the cotton and weigh it. Record the data in Table 1.
9. Subtract the weight of the cotton before heating from the weight of the cotton after heating to find the gain in weight of the cotton.

Data and Observations

Table 1

Weight of cotton after heating _____

Weight of cotton before heating _____

Weight gain by the cotton _____

Analysis

Write your answers to these questions on the back of this worksheet.

1. Why did the weight of the cotton increase?
2. Describe what the material on the cotton ball looks like. What do you think it might be?
3. Do filters prevent chemicals in smoke from getting into the lungs?
4. Even though filters may keep a small amount of chemicals from getting into the bodies of smokers, do you think the chemicals that come through the filter cause disease?
5. Do filters protect smokers from chemicals in cigarette smoke?

Further Investigation

Based on what you have learned today, how could you expand your experimental work?

Activity 14

Teaching the Health Lab

Use with Chapter 14, Lesson 1.

What Are the Effects of Alcohol on Fetal Development?

Objectives
- Compare data concerning the prenatal development of rats and mice exposed to alcohol and those not exposed to alcohol.
- Interpret data in terms of human development after prenatal exposure to alcohol.

Material
Graph paper

Time: One class period

Preparation
- Make copies of the student worksheet on page 32, one per student.
- Use this activity during the study of Lesson 1.

Teaching the Lab
1. Review the procedure with the students.
2. This lab may be done by students individually or by groups of students.

Analysis

PART A
1. Mouse A is alcohol exposed and has shorter distance between the nostrils.
2. Longer distance between mouth and nose
3. No indentation in upper lip

PART B
1. No
2. Without alcohol

3. Because rats and humans are both mammals, there may be similarities. Because human experiments of this nature could not be carried out for moral reasons, scientists must use the next best information.

Further Investigation
For interested students, re-create this table on the board. Have students analyze the data and answer the questions that follow.

Effects of Alcohol on 10-Day-Old Rat Fetuses			
Alcohol Exposure	Length (mm)	DNA Content (g)	Protein Content
Alcohol	4	23	223
No alcohol	5	33	333

1. After the rat is born, what might be the effect of less DNA? (body deformities and brain damage)
2. After the rat is born, what might be the effect of less protein? (body deformities, malfunctioning body chemistry, and less growth)
3. What might happen after birth to a rat that is smaller than all the others? (It would not be able to compete with siblings for food.)

Activity 14 — Health Lab

Use with Chapter 14, Lesson 1.

What Are the Effects of Alcohol on Fetal Development?

Introduction

When a pregnant woman drinks alcoholic beverages, her fetus may not develop normally. Children born to mothers who consumed alcohol regularly during pregnancy may have fetal alcohol syndrome. This disease causes facial deformities, mental retardation, small head size, and learning disabilities.

Objectives

- Compare data concerning development of rat and mouse embryos exposed to alcohol and those not exposed to alcohol.
- Interpret data in terms of human development after prenatal exposure to alcohol.

Material

Graph paper

Procedure

PART A

Examine the diagrams below. Diagram A is the head of a 14-day-old mouse fetus whose mother had alcohol in her diet. Diagram B is a 14-day-old mouse fetus whose mother was not exposed to alcohol. Tell three ways that the facial characteristics of mouse A differ from the facial characteristics of mouse B.

1. _____

2. _____

3. _____

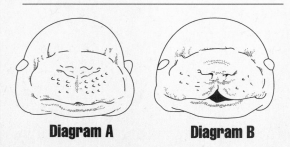

Diagram A   **Diagram B**

PART B

On the back of this worksheet, make a graph of the data in Table 1. Then answer the questions below.

Make a bar graph as follows. On the horizontal axis write *beer, wine, whiskey,* and *no alcohol.* On the vertical axis put the weight in grams. Make a bar for each type of alcoholic beverage.

Data and Observations

Table 1

Birth Weights of Rats Exposed to Alcohol Daily	
Alcohol Type	Weight (g)
Beer	4
Wine	5
Whiskey	4.9
No alcohol	6.0

Analysis

1. Is there an important difference in weight for the different types of alcohol?
2. Which rats had the highest birth weights?
3. Do you think predictions for humans exposed to alcohol before birth could be made based on studies with rats? Why or why not?

Further Investigation

Look up the latest information about fetal alcohol syndrome in recent health periodicals. Prepare a written report on your findings.

Activity 15 — Teaching the Health Lab

Use with Chapter 15, Lesson 1.

Using Prescription Drugs Safely

Objectives
- With a group, research one topic on the use of over-the-counter and prescription drugs.
- Prepare guidelines for safe and proper drug use.
- Combine guidelines with those of other groups to create a class booklet.

Materials
Library reference sources on drugs (e.g., *Complete Guide to Prescription and Non-Prescription Drugs,* edited by H. Winter Griffith, Body Press, 1994), and/or print-out sheets from a pharmacy on common prescription drugs

Labels from a variety of over-the-counter medications (e.g., aspirin, ibuprofen, anti-histamine, antacid, cold and flu aids)

Art supplies and paper

Time: Two to three class periods

Preparation
- Collect outer boxes or labels of over-the-counter medications.
- Locate reference sources for over-the-counter and prescription drugs.
- Contact a local pharmacist, nurse, doctor, and/or other health professional who may be able to speak to your class on using prescription and over-the-counter drugs properly.
- Make a copy of the student worksheet on page 34 for each student in class.

Teaching the Lab
1. Review the distinction between over-the-counter medications and prescription drugs. Then ask the class to suggest types of ailments that could be treated by a pain reliever or a germ fighter—such as muscular aches, headaches, intestinal problems, colds, and flu. List ideas on the board.
2. Ask for suggestions of types of over-the-counter medications that help relieve these problems—such as aspirin, ibuprofen, laxatives, antacids, cough syrups, and antihistamines. List these on the board. Using a reference, list common prescription drugs, such as amoxicillin, codeine, and penicillin.
3. Then have the class form five cooperative groups. Propose that each group create one part of a drug safety guide. Refer groups to their student worksheets for topics and to help plan their guide. For example, each group could work on a part of drug use, such as side effects, or on one or more over-the-counter drugs or prescription drugs.
4. As groups finish their parts of the project, have them write answers to the Analysis questions on the back of their worksheets.
5. Gather each group's report into one guide booklet for the classroom. If possible, make a copy for each student.

Analysis
Answers will vary.

Further Investigation
Encourage groups to research library periodicals for the most up-to-date medical information on common over-the-counter and prescription drugs. Have them add appropriate information to the class guide.

Activity 15

Health Lab

Using Prescription Drugs Safely

Introduction

Modern over-the-counter and prescription drugs can bring great relief to people suffering physical ailments. However, the variety of drugs available and their side effects make it difficult for many people to know how to use these medications properly and safely. A clear, brief, and comprehensive guide to common medications can be a welcome help.

Objectives

- With a group, research one topic on the use of over-the-counter and prescription drugs.
- Prepare guidelines for safe and proper drug use.
- Combine guidelines with those of other groups to create a class booklet.

Materials

Library reference sources on over-the-counter and prescription drugs (see your teacher for help)
Variety of over-the-counter packages and labels
Art supplies and paper

Procedure

1. Discuss with your classmates various common over-the-counter and prescription drugs and the problems they are meant to relieve. Draw up a list of the over-the-counter drugs and prescription drugs mentioned.
2. Using the topic outline on this page, decide with your classmates how you want to divide the research topics for the class guide.
3. With your group, you may want to further divide responsibilities. Ask your teacher for help with reference sources, if your group needs them.

4. When you have completed your research, work together to write your part of the guide. Be sure your information is brief and clear.
5. With your group, answer the Analysis questions on this page to help you complete your report.
6. Your teacher will collect all group reports into one class booklet.

Topic Outline

I. Common Over-the-Counter Drugs
   A. Purpose (e.g., relief from colds and flu, intestinal problems, allergies, headaches)
   B. Form (e.g., tablet, liquid)
   C. Brand names
II. Common Prescription Drugs
   A. Purpose (e.g., germ fighting, relief from different types of pain, relief from allergies)
   B. Form (e.g., tablet, liquid)
   C. Brand names
III. Use of Drug
   A. Dosage and frequency
   B. Dose for different age groups
   C. How to take the medication
IV. Warnings and Possible Side Effects
V. Storage and Disposal
VI. Poisoning Measures

Analysis

1. Is the purpose of your portion of the guide clearly identified?
2. Is your information complete? What questions might be answered by your part of the guide?
3. Why is your part of the guide important?

Further Investigation

How can you keep the information in your guide up-to-date?

Teaching the Health Lab   Use with Chapter 16, Lesson 4.

What Are Bicycle Safety Features?

Objectives
- Identify bicycle safety features.
- Demonstrate knowledge of bicycle safety features.

Materials
Scissors, one pair per student
Glue
One bicycle
Bicycle helmet
Cycling gloves
Helmet mirror
Flashing belt beacons
Reflective tape or ankle straps
Pant clip
Skateboard knee pads
Toe clips
Cycling goggles

Time: One class period

Preparation
- Make copies of the student worksheets on pages 36 and 37, one per student.
- Use this activity after students have completed their study of Chapter 16.
- Arrange for a student to bring in a bicycle for use during the demonstration.
- Borrow from a student, a bicycle shop, or a sporting goods store the bicycle safety equipment listed in the Materials section.
- Ask a student to help with the demonstration in Part A. He or she should wear white and bright colors on the day of the demonstration. Ask him or her to put on the safety equipment. Have the student mount the bicycle at the front of the classroom so that students can answer question 3 in Part A. Ask a volunteer to help steady the bicycle while the student is mounted.

Teaching the Lab
1. Review the procedure with the students.
2. Answers for Part A, items 1–3, will vary.
3. For Part B, as an alternative, you may wish to have students simply draw lines to indicate where each piece of safety equipment goes on the bicycle illustration.
4. Have students write their answers to all questions on a separate sheet of paper.

Analysis
1. A. Flag makes rider visible in traffic when another vehicle may block view of actual bicycle.
   B. Horn or bell signals to pedestrians from behind.
   C. Light makes cyclist more visible, especially at night.
   D. Rearview mirror allows rider to see what is approaching from the rear.
2. Light
3. Light
4. With the flow of traffic
5. All traffic lights and signs
6. White and reflective
7. When seated, the fully extended leg, with slightly bent knee, should allow the heel to touch the lowest point of the pedal.
8. No
9. Doors opening, passengers exiting, children running out from behind car, car pulling out into traffic

Further Investigation
With an expert present, have one bicycle per group, and check brakes, chains, and pedals for safety. Ask a bicycle racer to come in and demonstrate the features of racing bicycles and talk about racing. Ask a police officer to come and talk about bicycle safety.

Activity 16 — Health Lab

Use with Chapter 16, Lesson 4.

What Are Bicycle Safety Features?

Introduction

The wind whips your hair as you hurtle down a steep hill on your bicycle. Your hands sweat as you grip the handle bars. This is what summer is all about. Out of nowhere, a stop sign appears at the bottom of the hill. Brakes screech. Metal crunches. You wake up in traction in the hospital. You are lucky. You were not one of the 1000 bicycle deaths in this country each year. Many of these deaths could be prevented by following bicycle safety rules and making sure bicycles are equipped with proper safety features.

Objectives

- Identify bicycle safety features.
- Demonstrate knowledge of bicycle safety features.

Materials

Scissors
Glue

Procedure

PART A: A REAL BICYCLE AND RIDER

1. Observe the bicycle and rider in your classroom. This student is equipped with safety equipment. On a separate sheet, write a list of the safety equipment the rider is wearing.
2. Closely examine the bicycle, and compare it to the diagram in your book on page 501. Tell what safety features the bicycle is missing.
3. If a bicycle fits the rider, when seated, the rider should be able to extend the leg with knee slightly bent, and have the heel on the pedal at its lowest point. Does this bicycle fit this rider?

PART B: A PAPER BICYCLE

1. Cut out the bicycle safety equipment on your worksheet. Be sure that you can identify each of these items: flag, underseat reflector, rearview mirror, belt beacon, bell, headlight, toe clip, wheel reflectors, gloves, goggles, helmet, knee pads, and ankle strap.
2. Study the bicycle diagram in your textbook. Glue the safety equipment in place on the diagram of the bicycle and rider on your worksheet.

Analysis

1. What equipment is optional on a bicycle? Tell how each of these features could protect a rider.
2. What should replace the white reflector when riding at night?
3. What should replace the back reflector when riding at night?
4. Should you ride against the flow of traffic or with the flow of traffic?
5. Which traffic lights and signs must you obey?
6. What type of clothing is best to wear if you ride at night?
7. How do you tell if the bicycle seat is the correct height?
8. Is it safe to ride beside another cyclist?
9. Explain how a parked car could be a danger to a cyclist.

Further Investigation

Based on what you have learned today, how could you expand your investigation?

Health Lab • Activity 16   (continued)

Teaching the Health Lab

Use with Chapter 17, Lesson 3.

Practicing First Aid

Objectives
- Learn and practice techniques for tying slings and bandages.
- Demonstrate first-aid methods.

Materials
Standard first-aid book, available from the American Red Cross (one or more copies)
Small towels
Squares and strips of cloth
Safety pins

Time: One class period

Preparation
- Squares and strips of cloth can be made from old sheets or other scrap cloth. You may wish to ask students to help collect these materials.
- Make a copy of the student worksheet on page 39 for each student in class.
- Use the American Red Cross first-aid book as a reference and source of additional information.

Teaching the Lab
1. Review with students the first-aid procedures described in their texts for broken bones, sprains, and burns.
2. Have the class form small cooperative groups of at least four students. Provide each group with a large square, a small square, and strips of cloth.
3. Have students examine the pictures on their worksheets. Offer the first-aid books for those who want further information.
4. Have group members take turns playing the part of the victim. Other members will practice bandage ties for making a triangular bandage arm sling, making an ankle bandage, and anchoring a bandage over a burn.
5. Call on a group to come to the front of the class. Describe an injury that can be treated with one of the procedures practiced. Have the group demonstrate the proper procedure. Continue with other groups.
6. Have groups work together to write answers to the Analysis questions on the back of their worksheets.
7. Allow the class an opportunity to discuss their answers. Ask: Why is it important to have confidence that you can help someone in an emergency?

Analysis
Answers will vary, depending on students' experience.

Further Investigation
Encourage groups to use the first-aid book to investigate additional emergency procedures. Invite them to give an oral report on what they have learned.

Health Lab

Use with Chapter 17, Lesson 3.

Practicing First Aid

Introduction

Being able to help someone who is injured takes knowledge of and skill in using first aid. Such skill comes from practicing different first-aid procedures. Once you know what to do, you can confidently offer help where needed.

Objectives

• Practice techniques for tying slings and bandages.
• Demonstrate first-aid procedures.

Materials

Small towels
Squares and strips of cloth
Safety pins

Procedure

1. Your teacher will provide you with different-size cloth pieces to use for a sling and bandages.
2. Take turns playing the part of an accident victim. Use the cloth pieces to practice the different first-aid procedures shown on this page.
3. As a group, demonstrate for the class a first-aid procedure for an injury described by your teacher.

Analysis

1. Which first-aid procedure was the most difficult to learn? Why?
2. In what types of situations would these procedures be useful?

Further Investigation

What would you like to learn about other first-aid procedures?

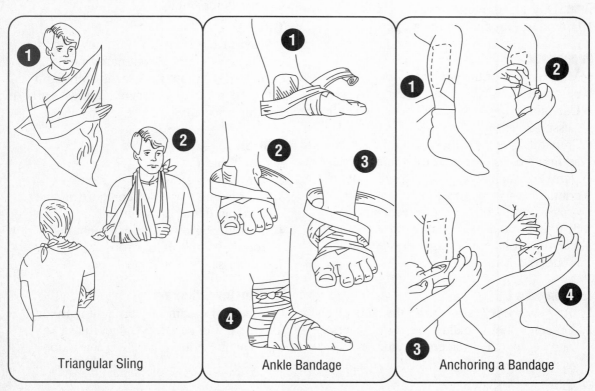

Triangular Sling   Ankle Bandage   Anchoring a Bandage

Activity 18 Teaching the Health Lab

Use with Chapter 18, Lesson 2.

How Does Detergent Affect Seed Germination?

Objectives
- Determine the effect of liquid detergent on seed germination.
- Compare the effect of detergent on germinating seeds to the germination of seeds not exposed to detergent.

Materials
Masking tape
Scissors, 1 pair per group
Petri dishes, 2 per group
Toothpicks, 1 per group
Paper towels, 1 per group
Radish seeds, 30 per group
Tap water in a large beaker
50-mL graduated cylinder
5 percent dishwashing detergent solution
Metric rulers, 1 per group
Graph paper

Time: Day 1: half a class period; Days 2–4: 10 minutes; Day 5: half a class period

Preparation
- Make copies of the student worksheets on pages 41 and 42, one per student.
- Use this activity after students have studied Lesson 2.
- Prepare a 5 percent detergent solution by adding 5 parts detergent to 95 parts water.
- Purchase radish seeds. Packets usually contain about 50 seeds.
- There is little difference in results among different brands of liquid detergent. Select a detergent labeled phosphate-free and biodegradable.

Teaching the Lab
1. Review the procedure with the students.
2. Students should make sure their fingers and graduated cylinders are free of detergent when handling seeds, water, and paper toweling.

3. This lab will work best if you can begin on a Monday.
4. If you do not meet with your class each day of the week, you may still set up the experiment one day and several days later make the observations.
5. As students observe growth of the root, fuzzy white growth will appear to cover the root. Explain that these are root hairs that soak up water.

Sample Hypothesis: Detergent will slow down or stop the germination of seeds.

Sample Data

Table 1
Day 1—no germination; Day 2—about 8 seeds in water; Day 3—about 15 in water; Day 4—about 22 in water, a few in detergent solution; Day 5—about 24 in water, several more in detergent.

Table 2
Water: Roots may be 6-12 mm long after 2–3 days; substantial root hair growth. Detergent solution: Few seeds will germinate. They may crack open, but most will not develop normally.

Analysis
1. See Table 1.
2. It inhibited growth.
3. It provided a basis of comparison for seeds in detergent solution.
4. Seedlings growing in detergent had fewer root hairs and shorter roots.
5. Fewer seeds would germinate.

Further Investigation
Conduct the same experiment with different types of seeds. Conduct the same experiment with different concentrations of detergent.

Activity 18 Health Lab

Use with Chapter 18, Lesson 2.

How Does Detergent Affect Seed Germination?

Introduction

When we wash clothing and dishes, the wastewater eventually finds its way back to our rivers, streams, and lakes. Even though the wastewater is treated, detergents may remain in the water. Detergents contain chemicals that soften the water and prevent dirt from being redeposited onto the clothing during washing. These chemicals may affect plant growth in a variety of ways. In this lab, you will examine the effect of detergents on seeds as they germinate.

Objectives

• Determine the effect of liquid detergent on seed germination.
• Compare the effect of detergent on germinating seeds to the germination of seeds not exposed to detergent.

Materials

Masking tape
Scissors, 1 pair per group
Petri dishes, 2 per group
Toothpick, 1 per group
Paper towel, 1 per group
Radish seeds, 30 per group
Tap water in a large beaker
50-mL graduated cylinder
Dishwashing detergent solution
Metric ruler
Graph paper

Procedure

1. Label one petri dish *water;* label the other *detergent.* Put your name on both lids.
2. Cut four circles of paper toweling to fit the bottoms of the dishes. Place two circles in the bottom of each dish.
3. Scatter 30 radish seeds evenly in each dish.
4. Before using the graduated cylinder, make sure it is completely free of detergent by rinsing it thoroughly. Measure and pour 10 mL of tap water into the dish labeled *water.*
5. Measure and pour 10 mL of the detergent solution into the petri dish labeled *detergent.*
6. Use a toothpick to reposition your seeds if necessary. Make sure that you use the toothpick in the plain water dish first so that the detergent is not introduced into that dish.
7. Replace the lids on the petri dishes, and seal them with two short pieces of masking tape on opposite sides of the dish.
8. Place the dishes in a warm, dark place.
9. Make a hypothesis that will predict the effects of detergents on the germination of seeds.
10. Observe your petri dishes each day for five days. Count the number of seeds germinated each day in each dish. Germination has occurred if the root is visible. Record your counts in Table 1 in the Data and Observations section. Observe and measure the roots of some of the germinated seedlings. Record your measurements in Table 2.
11. Do not allow the paper towels in the petri dishes to dry out. Add small amounts of water or detergent solution to the petri dishes as necessary.
12. After collecting data for five days, make a line graph on your graph paper from the data in Table 1. Place the number of days on the horizontal axis and the number of germinated seeds on the vertical axis. Plot the number of seeds that germinated during the five-day period. Make the detergent line on the graph with pencil and the water line with pen.

Health Lab • Activity 18   (continued)

Data and Observations

Table 1

Number of Seeds Germinated		
Day	Water	Detergent Solution
1		
2		
3		
4		
5		

Table 2

Growth of Germinating Seeds (in mm)		
Day	Water	Detergent Solution
1		
2		
3		
4		
5		

Analysis

1. How many seeds germinated after five days in water? In detergent solution?
2. How did the detergent affect germination of the seeds?
3. What was the importance of the petri dish with plain water?
4. What were the differences in the two petri dishes in the growth of the roots after five days?
5. Farmers often water their crops with untreated water from lakes and streams. What would happen to germinating seeds if the water used for crops contained detergent?

Further Investigation

Based on what you have learned today, how could you expand your experimental work?